The Aliens

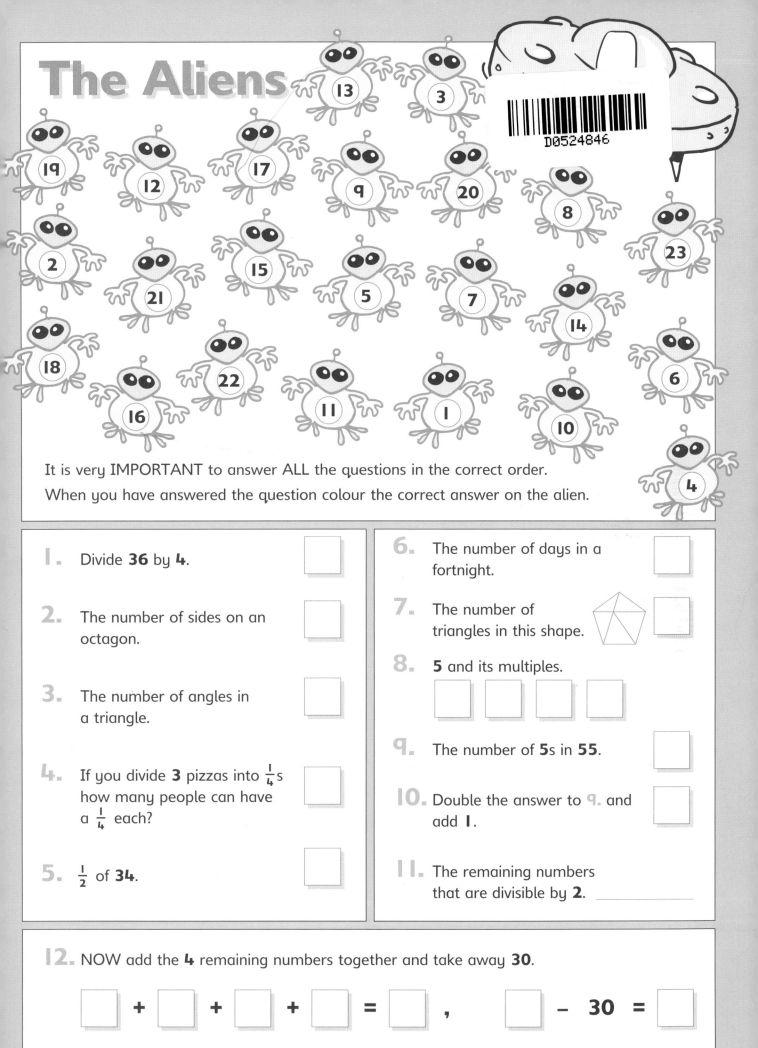

It is very IMPORTANT to answer ALL the questions in the correct order.

When you have answered the question colour the correct answer on the alien.

1. Divide **36** by **4**.

2. The number of sides on an octagon.

3. The number of angles in a triangle.

4. If you divide **3** pizzas into $\frac{1}{4}$s how many people can have a $\frac{1}{4}$ each?

5. $\frac{1}{2}$ of **34**.

6. The number of days in a fortnight.

7. The number of triangles in this shape.

8. **5** and its multiples.

9. The number of **5**s in **55**.

10. Double the answer to 9. and add **1**.

11. The remaining numbers that are divisible by **2**. _____

12. NOW add the **4** remaining numbers together and take away **30**.

☐ + ☐ + ☐ + ☐ = ☐ , ☐ − 30 = ☐

Write the answer on the spaceship door.

Time

1.

The netball match started at **2.30**p.m. They played for **35** minutes in each half, with a break for **20** minutes. What time did the game finish?

2.

Eating lunch for the whole school took **1**hr **10**mins. Then there was **20** mins. playtime. They went back into class at **1.15**p.m. What time did lunch break start?

3.

School finished at **3.30**p.m.

a. After School Club lasted $2\frac{1}{2}$ hours. So Archie left school at

b. He arrived home at **6.25**p.m. How long did it take him to get home?

4.

a. "Dumbo the Elephant" started at **7.05**p.m. and finished at **9.35**p.m. How long was the film?

b. It took **20** minutes to travel home from the cinema. At what time did they arrive home?

Schofield & Sims

KS2 Problem Solving 3

Name

Schofield & Sims

KS2 Problem Solving Book 3

written by Anne Forster and Paul Martin

PROBLEM SOLVING is a series of four workbooks.

Book One   978 07217 0935 2

Book Two   978 07217 0936 9

Book Three   978 07217 0937 6

Book Four   978 07217 1138 6

Notes for the teacher

The purpose of this series of books is to encourage and develop problem solving skills. Each book contains a series of carefully structured well-graded problems covering the Key Stage 2 mathematics curriculum. Both Number Problems and Word Problems, in computation, money, shape, area and measurement are presented attractively, helping to develop and extend a child's conceptual skills. Child-based contexts help to motivate the child to solve problems in their everyday experiences, using mathematical concepts in a practical way.

This book includes problems suitable for children in Years 5 and 6, in the following areas of mathematics: Number, Fractions, Ratio, Percentages, Money, Time, Shape, Measures, Area, Perimeter, Symmetry, Coordinates and Handling Data.

© 2005 Schofield & Sims Ltd

978 07217 0937 6

First printed 2005
Thirteenth impression 2013

Printed in the UK by Wyndeham Gait Ltd, Grimsby, Lincolnshire.

Design by www.ledgardjepson.com

Pinboards

Find four different ways of halving the area of a **6** × **6** pinboard. An example is done for you.

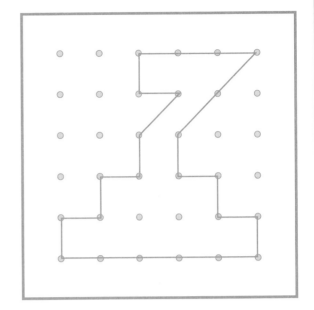

Number Puzzles

1. I thought of a number and then doubled it.

The answer was **30**.

What was the number I thought of?

2. How many squares are there?

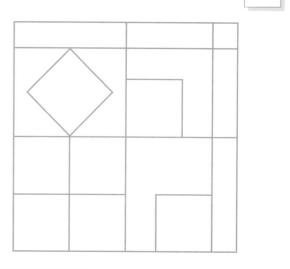

3. Make each line add up to **24**.

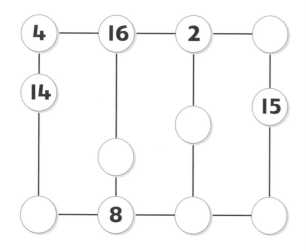

4. What is the total of the numbers on the unseen sides of each dice?

a. ☐

b. ☐

c. Add the **2** totals together. ☐

5.

 5   10   4 2 7

Choose from these balls and any operations to make these answers.

a. **57** _____

b. **49** _____

c. **36** _____

d. **75** _____

6. I found between **20** and **30** acorns.

I counted the acorns in **5**s and there were **2** left over.

I counted them in **2**s and there was **1** left over.

How many acorns did I have? ☐

All Animals

1. Three spiders caught a total of **35** flies in their webs.

Spider 1	**Spider 2**	**Spider 3**

Each spider caught a different odd number of flies. How many did each spider catch?
Find **5** different ways to catch them.

Spider 1	Spider 2	Spider 3	Total
			35
			35
			35
			35
			35

2. Mrs Barker has **3** dogs.

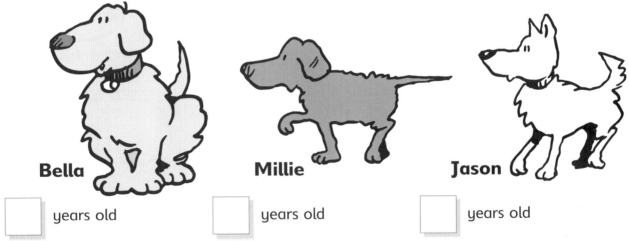

Bella	**Millie**	**Jason**

☐ years old   ☐ years old   ☐ years old

The total of Bella's and Jason's ages is **18** years.

The total of Millie's and Jason's ages is **9** years.

The total of all their ages is **20** years.

How old is each dog? Write their ages in the boxes.

Birthdays

1. This recipe is for **3** cakes. Re-write the recipe so that only **2** cakes can be made.

Recipe for **3** cakes	
750g	Flour
375g	Margarine
525g	Sugar
6	Eggs
270g	Cherries
180g	Walnuts
450g	Sultanas
1·5kg	Bananas

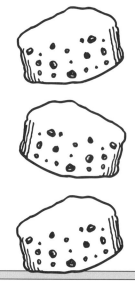

Recipe for **2** cakes	
500g	Flour
	Margarine
	Sugar
	Eggs
	Cherries
	Walnuts
	Sultanas
	Bananas

2. There are **27** candles to share among **3** cakes. Dick's cake has a multiple of **6** candles. Joe's has an odd number and Bob's has an even number of candles.

a. Write the number of candles there could be on each cake.

Dick 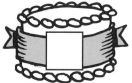 **Joe** 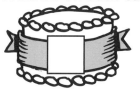 **Bob**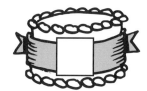

b. Find another way of putting the candles on the cakes.

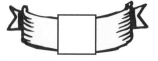 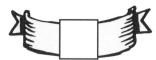 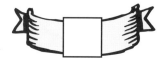

3. Find the area of each of these birthday cards.

c. 15cm

a. 14cm

14cm

☐ cm²

b. 7cm

10cm

cm²

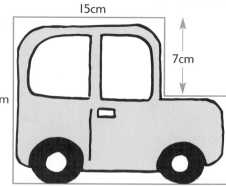

7cm

15cm

20cm

☐ cm²

d. 18cm

13cm

☐ cm²

Sponsored Swim

1. Three children in year **5** decided to do a sponsored swim for a Children's Charity. Complete the tables and work out the total amount collected by each child.

Name	Charlie	
Number of laps	**10**	
Sponsor	per lap	collected
Mum	**50p**	
Dad		**£10.00**
Uncle Fred	**25p**	
Auntie Olga	**75p**	
Gran		**£5.00**
Philip	**10p**	
Tim	**15p**	
Total amount collected		

Name	Anna	
Number of laps	**12**	
Sponsor	per lap	collected
Daddy	**£2.00**	
Grandpa	**50p**	
Nana	**£1.00**	
Mummy		**£21.00**
Josie	**30p**	
Rose	**25p**	
Fergus	**75p**	
Total amount collected		

Name	Nathan	
Number of laps	**8**	
Sponsor	per lap	collected
Mrs Smith	**40p**	
Jill	**60p**	
Dad	**£3.20**	
Mum	**£1.50**	
Grannie	**£1.60**	
Uncle Joe	**£2.60**	
Auntie Sue		**£14.00**
Total amount collected		

2. Who collected the most money? _____

3. How much money was collected altogether? _____

4. If Charlie had swum **12** laps how much would he have collected then? _____

5. Who paid Nathan the most? _____

6. How much more did he pay than Mrs Smith? _____

Favourite Wild Animals

1. **40** children were asked to choose their favourite wild animal. Using the fractions given work out how many children chose each animal. Complete the graph.

$\frac{3}{10}$ = ☐ **children**

$\frac{1}{20}$ = ☐ **children**

$\frac{9}{20}$ = ☐ **children**

$\frac{2}{10}$ = ☐ **children**

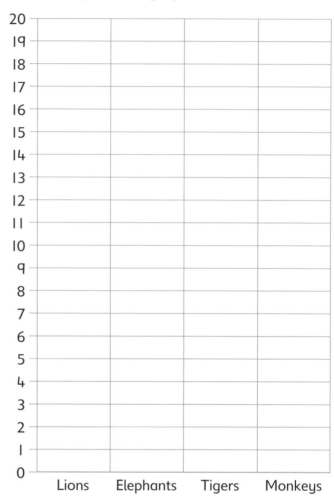

20			
19			
18			
17			
16			
15			
14			
13			
12			
11			
10			
9			
8			
7			
6			
5			
4			
3			
2			
1			
0			
Lions	Elephants	Tigers	Monkeys

2. If $\frac{1}{2}$ of the children who liked monkeys best changed their minds and decided they preferred elephants, how many then liked elephants best ☐ and monkeys best ☐ ?

3. If $\frac{1}{4}$ of the children who liked lions best changed their minds and then preferred tigers, how many children liked tigers best ☐ and lions ☐ best?

Shape

1. How many degrees in....

a. a whole turn? ▢

b. a $\frac{1}{4}$ turn? ▢

c. a $\frac{1}{2}$ turn? ▢

d. a $\frac{3}{4}$ turn? ▢

2. Which lines are parallel?

a. ▢ and ▢ , ▢ and ▢

b. Draw a line parallel to the remaining line.

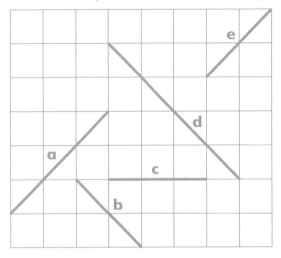

3. Draw a triangle with the same area as this green rectangle.

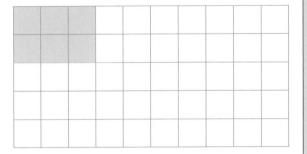

4. Complete the design of this bathroom floor by tessellating this tile shape.

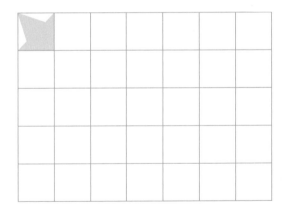

5. Draw the lines of symmetry on these shapes. Put a tick (✓) inside any shape which has no lines of symmetry.

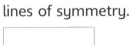

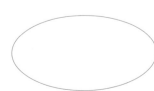
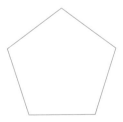

Temperature

1. **a.** Mark on the thermometer the weekly readings for the temperature at **2**p.m. on Fridays.

Mark with a green line **–5°**

        a blue line **–8°**

        a purple line **–1°**

        a yellow line **6°**

        a red line **8°**

b. What is the difference in temperature between the green line and the red line?

_____

c. **Temperature changes**

What is the change in the following temperatures?

	7a.m.	3p.m.	Change
Monday	2°	10°	
Tuesday	–3°	2°	
Wednesday	–5°		+11°
Thursday	1°		+12°
Friday		12°	+16°

```
20
19
18
17
16
15
14
13
12
11
10
 9
 8
 7
 6
 5
 4
 3
 2
 1
 0
–1
–2
–3
–4
–5
–6
–7
–8
–9
```

2. The graph shows the temperatures in the garden during a day in January.
Join the dots to complete the graph.

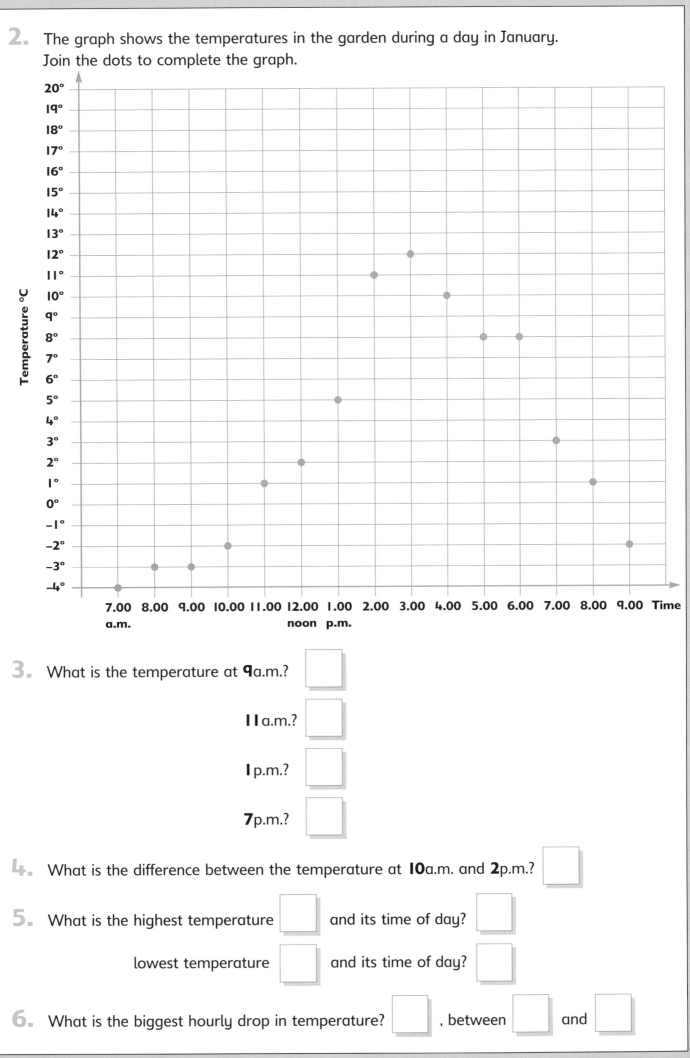

3. What is the temperature at **9** a.m.? ☐

I I a.m.? ☐

1 p.m.? ☐

7 p.m.? ☐

4. What is the difference between the temperature at **10** a.m. and **2** p.m.? ☐

5. What is the highest temperature ☐ and its time of day? ☐

lowest temperature ☐ and its time of day? ☐

6. What is the biggest hourly drop in temperature? ☐ , between ☐ and ☐

Number Puzzles

1. Use all the **6** digits to make an addition sum with the answer **819**

(**2**) (**3**) (**4**) (**5**) (**6**) (**7**)

[ ][ ][ ] + [ ][ ][ ] = **819**

2. Complete the loop by writing the missing numbers.

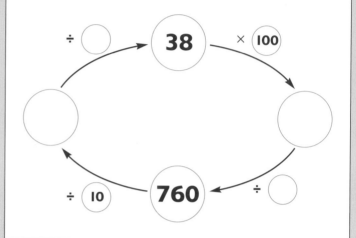

3.

a. What percentage of this shape is shaded?

[ ]

b. Colour red **10%** of this shape. Colour blue **40%** of the shape.

c. What percentage is not coloured?

[ ]

4. It took Dad **3**hrs to drive **180** miles to Blackpool.

a. What was his average speed?

[ ] mph

b. If the car travels **30** miles on **1** gallon of petrol how many gallons did Dad need? [ ] gallons

c. Petrol costs £**3.80** per gallon. How much did Dad's petrol cost?

[ ]

5. Oliver bought **12** tubes of fruit gums, which each contained **12** sweets. He gave his **18** friends **4** sweets each.

a. How many sweets were left? [ ]

b. How many tubes were left? [ ]

6. Complete the number chain.

(**7**) → ×8 → ( ) → ×7 → ( )

↓ × **25%**

( ) ← ÷7 ← ( ) ← × **0·5** ← ( )

Pull-out Answers

Page 3
1. **9**
2. **8**
3. **3**
4. **12**
5. **17**
6. **14**
7. **7**
8. **5, 10, 15, 20**
9. **11**
10. **23**
11. **6, 18 16, 22, 2, 4**
12. **21 + 19 + 13 + 1 = 54, 54 – 30 = 24**

Page 4
1. **4.00**p.m.
2. **11.45**a.m.
3. a. **6.00**p.m.
   b. **25** minutes
4. a. **$2\frac{1}{2}$** hours
   b. **9.55**p.m.

Page 5
Various answers for each pin board. Correct designs will all enclose areas of **$12\frac{1}{2}$** squares. E.g.

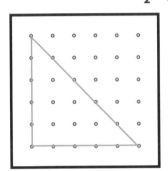 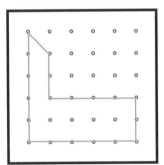

Page 6
1. **15**
2. **15**
3.

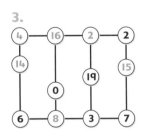

4. a. **12** b. **9**
   c. **21**
5. Various answers for each part, e.g.
   a. **(5 × 10) + 7**
   b. **(4 × 10) + 7 + 2**
   c. **(5 × 10) – (7 × 2)**
   d. **(7 × 10) + 5**
6. **27**

Page 7
1. Various answers in any order. Check that only odd numbers are used, and that in each row the number in each column is different. E.g.

Spider 1	Spider 2	Spider 3	Total
1	3	31	35
3	5	27	35
5	7	23	35
7	9	19	35
11	15	9	35

2. Bella **11**, Millie **2**, Jason **7**

Page 8
1. **500**g flour
   250g margarine
   350g sugar
   4 eggs
   180g cherries
   120g walnuts
   300g sultanas
   1kg bananas

2. Many possible answers e.g.

Dick	Joe	Bob
12	9	6
18	7	2

   (Dick can only have **6**, **12**, **18** or **24**; Joe can be any odd number, and the total of the **3** numbers must be **27**)

3. a. **196cm²**   b. **70cm²**   c. **265cm²**
   d. **234cm²**

Page 9
1.

Charlie (10)		
Mum	50p	£5.00
Dad	£1	£10.00
Uncle Fred	25p	£2.50
Auntie Olga	75p	£7.50
Gran	50p	£5.00
Philip	10p	£1.00
Tim	15p	£1.50
Total amount collected		£32.50

Anna (12)		
Daddy	£2.00	£24.00
Grandpa	50p	£6.00
Nana	£1.00	£12.00
Mummy	£1.75	£21.00
Josie	30p	£3.60
Rose	25p	£3.00
Fergus	75p	£9.00
Total amount collected		£78.60

Nathan (8)		
Mrs Smith	40p	£3.20
Jill	60p	£4.80
Dad	£3.20	£25.60
Mum	£1.50	£12.00
Grannie	£1.60	£12.80
Uncle Joe	£2.60	£20.80
Auntie Sue	£1.75	£14.00
Total amount collected		£93.20

2. Nathan
3. **£204.30**
4. **£39.00**
5. Dad
6. **£22.40**

Page 10

1.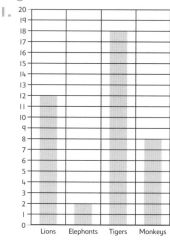

2. **6** liked elephants, **4** liked monkeys

3. **21** liked tigers, **9** liked lions

Page 11

1. a. **360°**
   b. **90°**
   c. **180°**
   d. **270°**

2. a. **a** and **e**; **b** and **d**
      (in any order)
   b. Any horizontal line will be parallel to line **c**

3. Any triangle with an area of **6** squares, e.g. base **3**, height **4** or base **6**, height **2** ...etc

4.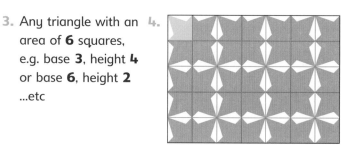

5.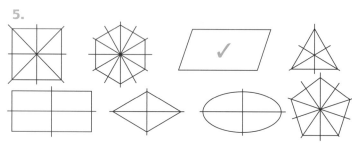

Page 12

1. a.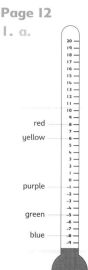
   b. **13°**
   c.

	7a.m.	3p.m.	Change
Monday	2°	10°	+8°
Tuesday	−3°	2°	+5°
Wednesday	−5°	6°	+11°
Thursday	1°	13°	+12°
Friday	−4°	12°	+16°

Page 13

2. Dots on graph joined with straight lines

3. a. **−3°**
   b. **1°**
   c. **5°**
   d. **3°**

4. **13°**

5. **12°** at **3:00**p.m.
   −4° at **7:00**a.m.

6. **5°** between **6**p.m and **7**p.m.

Page 14

1. Various answers, eg:
   576 + 243
   276 + 543
   246 + 573
   ... etc

2.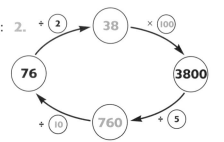

3. a. **50%**
   b. **2** red squares, **8** blue squares
   c. **50%**

4. a. **60** m.p.h.
   b. **6** gallons
   c. **£22.80**

5. a. **72**
   b. **6** tubes

6.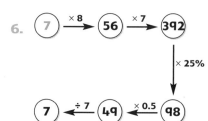

Page 15

1. **17**

2. between **3**p.m. and **4**p.m.

3. between **8**a.m. and **9**a.m.

4. **48**

5. between **9**a.m. and **10**a.m., and between **1**p.m. and **2**p.m.

6. **146**

Page 16

1. a. **£7.50**, **£3.00**, **£21.00**
   b. **£30.55**, **£61.10**, **£305.50**

2. a.

John		Sophie		Alphonse	
Floppies	£6.84	Cordless	£65.52	PC	£539.10
CD rom	£13.41	Paper	£4.50	Installation	£142.20
Notebook	£521.10	Photopaper	£24.30	Mouse	£23.22
Total	£541.35	Total	£94.32	Total	£704.52

   b. Alphonse

A2

Page 17

1.

2. **2** coloured orange
   4 coloured blue
   6 coloured red
   9 coloured yellow
   3 coloured green
   Fraction green = $\frac{3}{24}$ or $\frac{1}{8}$

3. plaice   **8**
   cod   **32**
   kippers   **8**
   salmon   **16**

Page 18

1. **£6**
2. **4**
3. **£21.65**
4. a. **£1.25**
   b. **£3.75**
5. **500**

Page 19

6. a. **35 000**   b. **24 000**
   c. **48 000**   d. **20 000**
   e. **36 000**   f. **35 000**
   g. **28 000**   h. **41 000**

7.
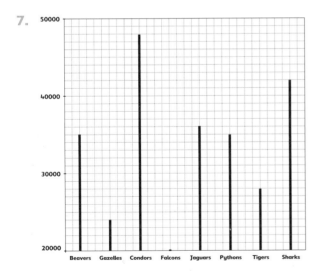

8. a. Condors
   b. Falcons
   c. **16 920, 8 425**
   d. **£1 195 075.00**
   e. **£862 750.00**
   f. **28 075**

Page 20

1. **£112.00**

2.

	cost	£20	£10	£5	£2	£1	50p	20p	10p	5p	2p	1p
Rabbit food × 2	£2.50				1		1					
Sawdust	£1.75					1	1	1		1		
Carrots × 7	49p							2		1	2	
Lettuce × 2	£1.16					1			1	1		1
Straw	£2.99			1			1	2		1	2	
Rabbit	£35	1	1	1								
Hutch	£75	3	1	1								
Bowl	£2				1							

3. 1 week   £**4.15**
   4 weeks £**16.60**
   1 year   £**215.80**

4. **£5.85**

Page 21

1.

	£10.00	£20.00	£50.00	£100.00
USA Dollar	17.20	34.40	86.00	172.00
Euro	14.30	28.60	71.50	143.00
Yen	1903.50	3807.00	9517.50	19035.00
Australian Dollar	24.30	48.60	121.50	243.00
Swedish Kronor	129.50	259.00	647.50	1295.00
South African Rand	114.40	228.80	572.00	1144.00
Swiss Franc	22.00	44.00	110.00	220.00
Canadian Dollar	22.50	45.00	112.50	225.00

2.

London Time	City	Local Time
16:25	Paris	17:25
12:50	San Francisco	04:50
21:00	New York	16:00
13:30	Amsterdam	14:30

Page 22
1. a. Total = **219 090**
   b. Average = **73 030**
2. a. USA
   b. China
   c. **330**

3. £**109.96** × 3 = £**329.88**

4. a. Yellow (**2**), Blue (**4**), Brown (**1**)
   b. **0·15**
   c. **0·35**
   d. **0·5**
5. a. **6**m **30·76**s
   b. **6**m **46·50**s
   c. **6**m **33·40**s
   d. **1·88**s

Page 23
6.

	Vault	Beam	Floor	Bars	Total	Position	Highest Personal Score
Anya	9·623	9·812	9·956	9·572	38·963	5	9·956
Kelly	9·848	9·918	9·899	9·937	39·602	3	9·937
Nina	8·924	9·659	9·729	9·886	38·198	6	9·886
Sophie	9·940	9·871	9·824	9·658	39·293	4	9·940
Olga	9·999	9·982	9·985	9·895	39·861	1	9·999
Elena	9·899	9·995	9·897	9·997	39·788	2	9·997

7. a. Ghana **39·11**, GB **38·43**, Greece **38·29**, Russia **38·25**
   b. **1**st lap Ghana, **3**rd lap Greece
   c. **1**st Russia, **2**nd Greece, **3**rd GB, **4**th Ghana
   d. **0·04** seconds

Page 24
1. **16 475**m
2. Ben Nevis **1343**m
3. **3295**m
4. **8460**m
5. **4040**m
6. **8237·5**m

Page 25
1. a. 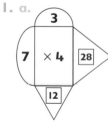   b. 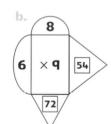   c.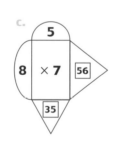

2. **12, 54, 72**
3. **12, 28, 72, 54, 56**

4.

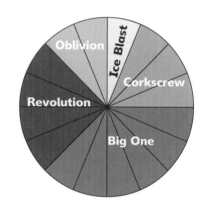

×	7	4	6	9	2	5	8	10	3
3	21	12	18	27	6	15	24	30	9
9	63	36	54	81	18	45	72	90	27
8	56	32	48	72	16	40	64	80	24
2	14	8	12	18	4	10	16	20	6
5	35	20	30	45	10	25	40	50	15
10	70	40	60	90	20	50	80	100	30
4	28	16	24	36	8	20	32	40	12
7	49	28	42	63	14	35	56	70	21
6	42	24	36	54	12	30	48	60	18

5. a. **100**
   b. **150**
6. a. **56**
   b. **84**

Page 26
1.

2. a. Big One
   b. Ice Blast
   c. Oblivion
   d. Revolution
   e. Oblivion

3.

	Big One	Corkscrew	Ice Blast	Revolution	Oblivion
Number of People	360	180	60	240	120

4.

	Big One	Corkscrew	Ice Blast	Revolution	Oblivion
Number of Adults	240	150	20	51	60
Number of Children	120	30	40	189	60

Page 27

1 3	2 5	3 7	■	4 5	5 4	7	6 5
7 6	0	1	8 2	■	0	■	2
0	■	■	9 5	10 3	6	11 2	■
■	12 5	13 7	1	9	■	14 2	15 4
16 3	1	3	4	■	17 5	8	6
8	■	2	■	18 6	3	■	2
19 6	3	5	■	20 4	2	8	■
21 9	7	■	22 8	8	5	0	0

A4

Garden Birds

The following graph shows the frequency of birds seen visiting the garden during each hour of the day.

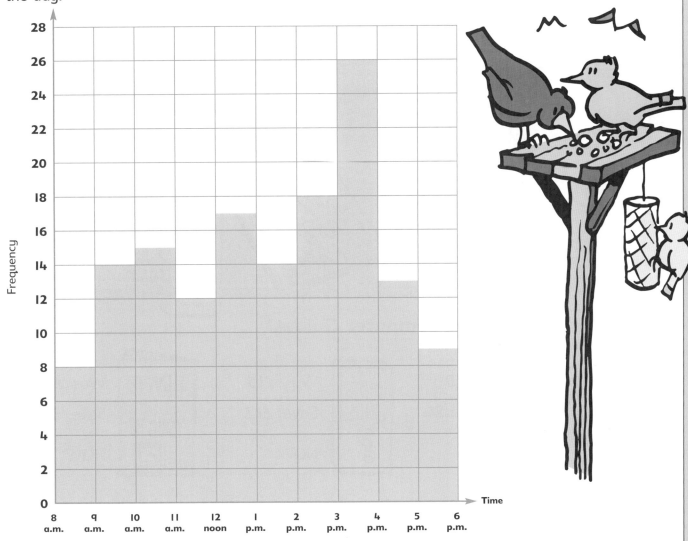

1. How many birds visited the garden between **12** noon and **1** p.m.?

2. During which hour did most birds visit?   Between _____ and _____

3. During which hour did least birds visit?   Between _____ and _____

4. How many fewer birds visited in the morning than the afternoon?

5. Twice during the day, the same number of birds visited. What times were these?

    Between _____ and _____ , and between _____ and _____

6. What is the total number of birds visiting the garden during the day?

Computer Fair

10 DISKETTE

Notebook £579.00

PAPER 1 REAM £5.00

Cordless keyboard £72.80

10 CDS £14.90

Floppy disks £7.60

PC £599.00

£27.00

PHOTO PAPER 100

USING THE INTERNET £10

IDIOTS GUIDE ? £15

£24 HOW TO USE YOUR PC

Mouse £25.80

Insurance 3 yrs £91.65

1.

a. **Summer Sale on Computer Guides!**

Write the new price in the box.

USING THE INTERNET

Was **£10**
Save **£2.50**
NOW ☐

IDIOTS GUIDE ?

Was **£15**
Save **£12**
NOW ☐

HOW TO USE YOUR PC

Was **£24**
Save **£3**
NOW ☐

b. How much does insurance cost for 1 year?_____ 2yrs?_____ 10 yrs?_____

GREAT BARGAINS

2.

a. Calculate these bills using sale prices with **10%** off.

John bought		Sophie bought		Alphonse bought	
with **10% OFF**	New Price	with **10% OFF**	New Price	with **10% OFF**	New Price
Floppy discs		Cordless keyboard		PC	
Box of CDs		Paper		Installation	
Notebook		Photographic paper		Mouse	
Total sale		Total sale		Total sale	

b. Who paid the largest bill? _____

All at Sea

1. **Decimal fractions.** Match the fractions to make a pair.

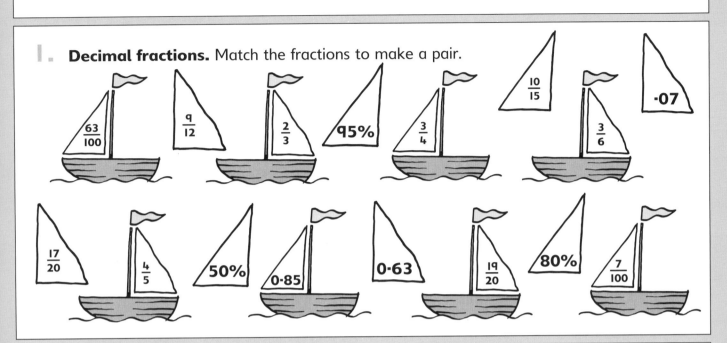

$\frac{63}{100}$ $\frac{9}{12}$ $\frac{2}{3}$ 95% $\frac{3}{4}$ $\frac{10}{15}$ $\frac{3}{6}$ ·07

$\frac{17}{20}$ $\frac{4}{5}$ 50%   0·85   0·63 $\frac{19}{20}$ 80% $\frac{7}{100}$

2. There are **24** fish in the aquarium.

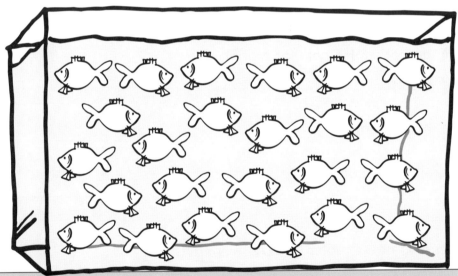

Colour $\frac{1}{12}$ orange

$\frac{1}{6}$ blue

25% red

$\frac{3}{8}$ yellow

the rest green!

What fraction of the **24** fish is green?

3. Mr Fish sold his fish on his market stall. He sold **64** fish last Friday morning.
   Use the pie chart to find out how many of each type of fish were bought.

plaice ☐

cod ☐

kippers ☐

salmon ☐

cod

kippers

plaice

salmon

Football Match

1. Two adult tickets to the match cost the same as three children's tickets.

   If one adult ticket costs £9.00, what is the price of a child's ticket?

2. John went to the match with his friends. They shared a box

   of popcorn costing £4.86 and fish and chips costing £6.98.

   They each paid £2.96. How many children were there?

3. Ian had £12.69 left after paying for his ticket and his share of the snacks.

   How much did he have to start with?

4. John had £5 in coins in his pocket. He paid for a drink with

   2 × 50p, 2 × 10p and 1 × 5p.

   How much did he give the stall holder?

   How much did he have left in his pocket?

5. There were 1000 spectators at the match. If 20% were girls and

   30% were boys, how many adults were there?

6. Eight football teams had the following gates. Round the numbers to the nearest thousand.

a. **Beavers** **35290** _35 000_

b. **Gazelles** **23944** _____

c. **Condors** **47803** _____

d. **Falcons** **19728** _____

e. **Jaguars** **36305** _____

f. **Pythons** **34510** _____

g. **Tigers** **27880** _____

h. **Sharks** **40864** _____

Plot the bar line graph using the rounded numbers.

7.

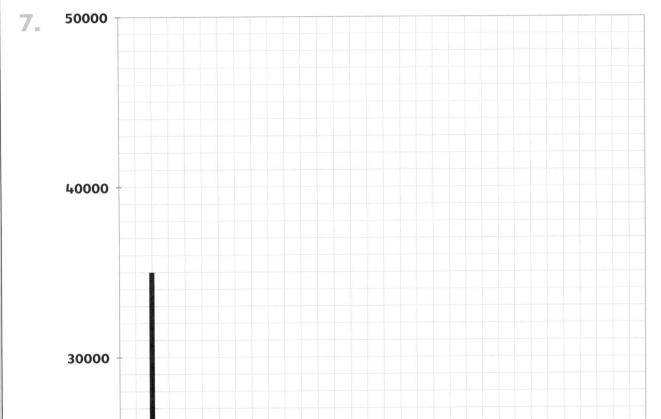

8. Use the original gate numbers to calculate the following answers.

a. Which team had the largest gate? _____

b. Which team had the smallest gate? _____

c. What is the difference between the gate numbers at:

Sharks and Gazelles? _____ Jaguars and Tigers? _____

d. The average price of a seat in the stands costs £**25**.
How much money was taken at the Condors game? _____

e. How much money was taken at the Pythons game? _____

f. What is the difference in the number of spectators
between the largest and smallest crowds? _____

Pets

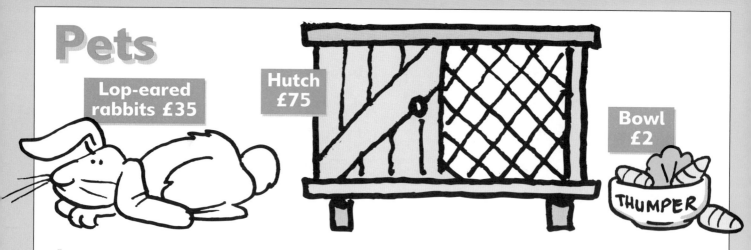

Lop-eared rabbits £35

Hutch £75

Bowl £2

THUMPER

1. Tom bought a lop-eared rabbit with its hutch and bowl.

   How much did he spend in total? _____

£1·25 RABBIT FOOD

£1·75 SAWDUST

7p each — carrots

lettuce 58p each

£2·99 STRAW

2. If you buy a pet rabbit you will have to pay for food and bedding each week. Show how you would pay for these for the **1**st week. This cost will include the rabbit, hutch and bowl. Use the smallest number of notes and coins in each case.

	cost	£20	£10	£5	£2	£1	50p	20p	10p	5p	2p	1p
Rabbit food × 2												
Sawdust												
Carrots × 7												
Lettuce × 2												
Straw												
Rabbit												
Hutch												
Bowl												

3. What is the total cost of food for a week? _____

   4 weeks? _____

   a year? _____

4. Mum pays for the straw and sawdust, but you pay for the food each week. If you have £10 a week pocket money how much would you have left after paying the weekly cost?

   _____

The Airport

The Airport Bank displays currency exchange for £1.00.

1. Work out how much of each currency you could get for £10, £20, £50 and £100.

Rates of Exchange

	£1.00
USA Dollar	1.72
Euro	1.43
Yen	190.35
Australian Dollar	2.43
Swedish Kronor	12.95
South African Rand	11.44
Swiss Franc	2.20
Canadian Dollar	2.25

	£10.00	£20.00	£50.00	£100.00
USA Dollar				
Euro				
Yen				
Australian Dollar				
Swedish Kronor				
South African Rand				
Swiss Franc				
Canadian Dollar				

2. Airport timetables use the **24** hour clock. Find the arrival times in the following cities, given that Paris and Amsterdam are **1** hour ahead of London. New York is **5** hours behind London and San Francisco is **8** hours behind London.

London Time	City	Local Time
16:25	Paris	
12:50	San Francisco	
21:00	New York	
13:30	Amsterdam	

Olympics

1. Find the average points scored by the **3** medallists.

74,663	72,927	71,500
Gold	**Silver**	**Bronze**

Total score = ☐

Average score = ☐

2. Look at the medal table.

	Gold	Silver	Bronze
Australia	17	16	16
China	32	17	14
USA	31	39	30
Russia	27	22	39
GB	9	9	12

Who won the most medals? _____

Who won the most gold? _____

How many medals are shown on this table? ☐

3. Find the total cost of cycling equipment.

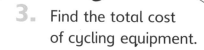

Helmet **£14.99**

Shirt **£19.99**

Gloves **£39.99**

Shorts **£34.99**

What is the total cost for the **3** medallists?

☐ **× 3 =** ☐

4. The diver with the highest points wins.

  a. Circle the medallists

    gold → yellow

    silver → blue

    bronze → brown

  1. 589·63

2. 590·13   3. 581·64

4. 589·98   5. 580·03

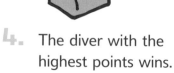

Find the difference between

  b. gold and silver _____

  c. silver and bronze _____

  d. gold and bronze _____

5. The rower with the lowest times wins.

m = minutes   s = seconds

6m 46·50s

6m 33·40s   6m 34·24s

6m 30·76s   6m 32·64s

6m 39·74s

  a. Gold medal time _____

  b. Slowest time _____

  c. Bronze medal time _____

  d. How far behind was the silver from the gold?

_____

Gymnastics

6. Complete the table below.

	Vault	Beam	Floor	Bars	Total	Position	Highest Personal Score
Anya	9·623	9·812	9·956	9·572			
Kelly	9·848	9·918	9·899	9·937			
Nina	8·924	9·659	9·729	9·886			
Sophie	9·940	9·871	9·824	9·658			
Olga	9·999	9·982	9·985	9·895			
Elena	9·899	9·995	9·897	9·997			

Men's 4 × 100m Relay Race

7. This table shows the time taken in seconds by each runner.
Work out each team's total time.

a.

		Ghana	GB	Greece	Russia
Leg	1	9·04	9·16	9·59	9·29
	2	10·25	10·03	9·12	9·53
	3	10·26	10·22	10·19	10·28
	4	9·56	9·02	9·39	9·15
Total					

b. Who was leading after the **1**st leg? _____

3rd leg? _____

c. List the teams in the finishing order.   **1**st _____   **2**nd_____

3rd _____   **4**th _____

d. By how much did the **1**st team win? _____

Mountain Scenery

1,343m	390m	8,850m	1,082m	4,810m
Ben Nevis	**Sugar Loaf**	**Everest**	**Table Mountain**	**Mont Blanc**

1. What is the total height of the **5** mountains?

_____

2. Which is the median height?

_____

3. What is the mean height of the mountains?

_____

4. What is the range in height between the highest and the lowest mountains?

_____

5. What is the difference in height between the **2** highest mountains?

_____

6. If a mountaineer climbed $\frac{1}{2}$ way up each mountain how far would he have climbed in total?

_____

Multiplication

1. Complete the multiplication machines.

a. 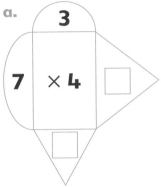   b. 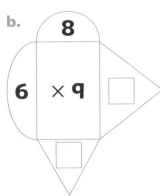   c.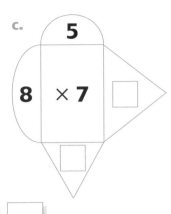

2. List the multiples of **3** that are in the answer boxes. ☐ ☐ ☐

3. List the multiples of **2**. ☐ ☐ ☐ ☐ ☐

4. Complete the following multiplication table.

×	7		6	9		5			
			18	27					
9		36				72			
8				16		64			
				4					
						40			15
		40						100	
			36						
				14					
								60	

5. There are **25** small Easter Eggs in a box.

   a. How many Easter Eggs are there in **4** boxes? ☐

   b. Mrs Clegg bought **6** boxes. How many eggs did she buy? ☐

6. There are **28** rabbits in a field. Half of the rabbits have **4** babies each.

   a. How many more rabbits are there now? ☐

   b. How many rabbits are there in total? ☐

Sherwood Park

1. This pie chart is divided into **16** equal parts. Complete the pie chart by using the information below. Use a different colour for each ride.

    $\frac{1}{16}$ Ice Blast

    $\frac{3}{16}$ Corkscrew

    $\frac{6}{16}$ Big One

    $\frac{1}{4}$ Revolution = $\frac{\square}{16}$

    $\frac{1}{8}$ Oblivion = $\frac{\square}{16}$

2. a. Which is the most popular ride? _____

    b. Which is the least popular ride? _____

    c. Which ride is twice as popular as Ice Blast? _____

    d. Which ride is **25**% of the chart? _____

    e. Which ride is $\frac{1}{2}$ as popular as Revolution? _____

3. 60 people went on Ice Blast. Work out how many people went on each of the other rides using the information in the pie chart.

	Big One	Corkscrew	Ice Blast	Revolution	Oblivion
Number of People	◯	◯	**60**	◯	◯

4. Work out how many adults and children went on each ride.

	Big One	Corkscrew	Ice Blast	Revolution	Oblivion
Number of Adults	◯	**150**	◯	◯	◯
Number of Children	**120**	◯	**40**	**189**	**60**

Cross Numbers

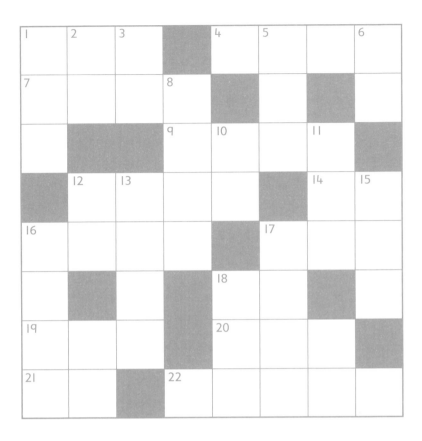

You may need a calculator!

Answer the clues to complete the puzzle.

Across

1. **7 × 51**
4. A shelf holds **365** books. There are **15** shelves. How many books are there in total?
7. **1503 × 4**
9. Change **5·362** litres to ml
12. **10000 – 4281**
14. **1** litre of juice fills **6** glasses. How many glasses are there in **4** litres?
16. **3218 + 763 – 847**
17. **8204 ÷ 14**
18. $\frac{7}{10}$ of **90**
19. How many 5p in **£31.75**?
20. **627 – 199**
21. The largest prime number below **100**
22. Round **88459·3** to the nearest **100**

Down

1. How many degrees equal **4** right angles?
2. Number of years in $\frac{1}{2}$ a century
3. **120 – 7²**
5. **58 × 7**
6. The number of weeks in a year
8. **3000 – 486**
10. $\frac{3}{4}$ of a year in weeks
11. A car does **38** miles per gallon. If it uses **6** gallons on a journey how many miles does it travel?
12. **9** less than **5 × 12**
13. **293 × 25**
15. $\frac{3}{4}$ is **1386**. What is $\frac{1}{4}$?
16. To what do you add **2457** to make **6326**?
17. **213 × 25**
18. **81 × 8**

Schofield & Sims

the long-established educational publisher
specialising in maths, English and science materials for schools

Key Stage 2 Problem Solving is a series of graded activity books helping children to sharpen their mathematical skills. It encourages them to apply their maths skills to a range of 'real-life' situations, such as shopping and keeping score in games.

Key Stage 2 Problem Solving Book 3 covers:

- Rotation of shapes, lines of symmetry and tesellation
- Percentages
- Fractions
- Decimal numbers
- Time problems
- Ratio.

This book is suitable for children in Key Stage 2 – particularly those in Years 5 and 6.

The full range of titles in the series is as follows:

Key Stage 2 Problem Solving Book 1 (for Years 3 and 4)   ISBN 978 07217 0935 2

Key Stage 2 Problem Solving Book 2 (for Years 4 and 5)   ISBN 978 07217 0936 9

Key Stage 2 Problem Solving Book 3 (for Years 5 and 6)   ISBN 978 07217 0937 6

Key Stage 2 Problem Solving Book 4 (for Year 6)   ISBN 978 07217 1138 6

Have you tried **Mental Arithmetic** by Schofield & Sims?
This series helps children to sharpen their calculation skills by using mathematical knowledge to solve one- and two-step number problems.

For further information and to place your order
visit www.schofieldandsims.co.uk or telephone 01484 607080

ISBN 978-07217-0937-6

9 780721 709376

Schofield & Sims

Dogloy Mill, Fenay Bridge, Huddersfield HD8 0NQ
Phone: 01484 607080 Facsimile: 01484 606815
E-mail: sales@schofieldandsims.co.uk
www.schofieldandsims.co.uk

ISBN 978 07217 0937 6

£2.95
(Retail price)

Key Stage 2
Age range 7-11 years